Published simultaneously in 1992 by
Exley Publications Ltd in Great Britain
and Exley Giftbooks in the USA
Reprinted 1993
Copyright © Helen Exley, 1992
Selection © Helen Exley, 1992

Edited: Helen Exley
Illustrations: Juliette Clarke

ISBN 1-85015-345-0

Printed in Spain by Grafo S.A. – Bilbao.

Exley Publications Ltd, 16 Chalk Hill, Watford,
Herts WD1 4BN, United Kingdom.
Exley Giftbooks, 359 East Main Street, Suite 3D,
Mount Kisco, NY 10549, USA.

An illustrated

Country Lover's
Notebook

illustrated by Juliette Clarke
and edited by Helen Exley

EXLEY

MT. KISCO, NEW YORK • WATFORD, UK

April.
- Along the path on R. plant Pulmonaria and Primula.
- On corner under front window try either horizontal lavender or grey cotton lavender.
- Put clumps of small daffodils between shrubs at front under window / muscari /
- Along wall facing road - try climbing rose. primulas small daffodils-
- Along hedge try dog violets + larger daffodils
- By swing put tulips / daffodils.

April
Campanula - miniature. alpine below rocks.

Geranium - Johnsons blue - try under mahonia at front

Agapanthus - from pot try garage wall by freesion.

Put iris + nerine's in?
pebbles.

Try silver leaved
artemesia against
sedums or blue geranium

Try lamb's ear Stachys in pots with
busy lizzies or geraniums. Try with
blue geranium

Aubrieta with Oenothera.
Put sisyrinchium on R. back-garden
by Hosta -

Pot ideas

Summer

- Osteospermums

- Arum lilies in blue pot

. . . And time remembered is grief forgotten,
And frosts are slain, and flowers begotten,
And in green underwood and cover
Blossom by blossom the spring begins.
                    Algernon Charles Swinburne (1837-1909)

- Make a throw for chair under arch
  + re-cover 2 cushions for gazebo

Walk away quietly in any direction and taste the freedom of the mountaineer. . . . Climb the mountains and get their good tidings. Nature's peace will flow into you as sunshine flows into trees. The winds will blow their own freshness into you, and the storms their energy, while cares will drop off like autumn leaves.
John Muir (1838-1914)

Front border

Remove Penstemons

BORDER.
Purple
Limeish
Red/Purple

Iris

Mahonia

Yew-shaped

Fr. Lavender

Alchemilla

Pink potentilla

French Lavender

Purple Thyme

Purple

<u>Buy</u>   1 fr. Lavender

6 Globe - purple Alliums.

The front bedroom window

Hagley Hybrid. Clematis.
Rose - deep pink -
Ta

More than half a century has passed, and yet each spring, when I wander into the primrose wood and see the pale yellow blooms, and smell their sweetest of scents, . . . for a moment I am seven years old again and wandering in the fragrant wood.

Gertrude Jekyll (1843-1932)

The 'bank' 18 Hopyard

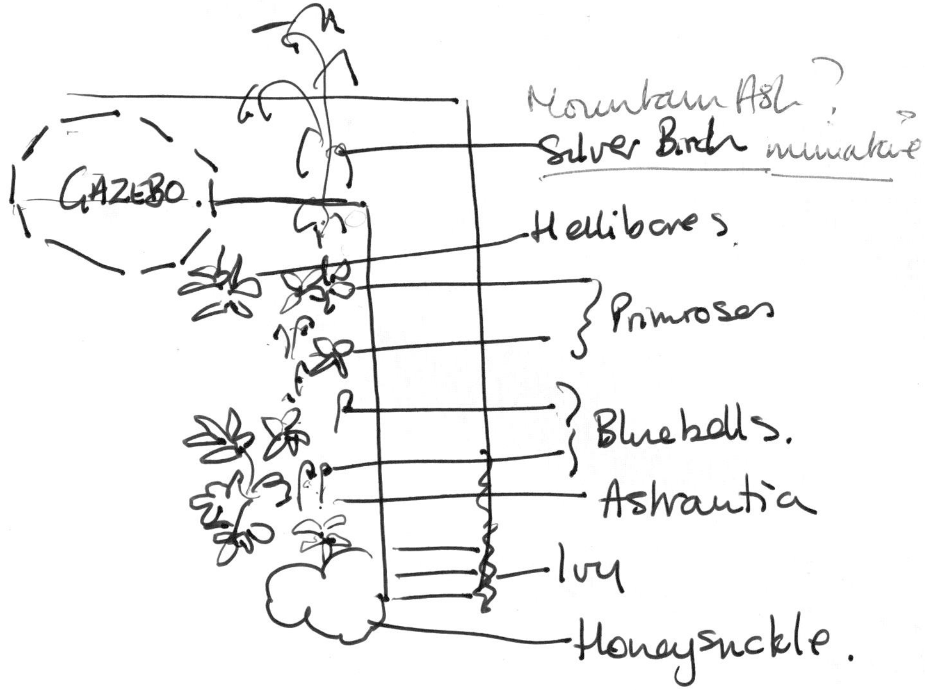

Mountain Ash?
Silver Birch miniature

GAZEBO.

Hellibores.

} Primroses

} Bluebells.

Astrantia

Ivy

Honeysuckle.

Astrantia - shade loving

Heaven is under our feet
as well as over our heads.
Henry David Thoreau
(1817-1862)

Fences
Taujutica Clematis
Siberica - 'Freckles'
Liies

Passiflora
Honeysuckle.

Dig up

Passiflora ?

Honeysuckle by gate .?

2 x roses ✓

2 x ~~clematis~~.

- shrub - back wall.

- ~~Large helebore seedling~~.

- ~~white~~ "

- ~~purple~~ "

- ~~heuchera~~

- bleeding heart. x small white

- astrantia.

- ~~clemat~~ cyclamen.

- day lilies - + ~~Delphiniums~~

Take cuttings

- Curry plant

- Rosemary

The clearest way into the Universe is through a forest wilderness.

John Muir (1838-1914)

The forest is a peculiar organism of unlimited kindness and benevolence that makes no demands for its sustenance and extends generously the products of its life activity; it affords protection to all beings, offering shade even to the axeman who destroys it.

Gautama Buddha (c.563-c.483 B.C.)

Simplicity in all things is the secret of the wilderness and one of its most valuable lessons. It is what we leave behind that is important. I think the matter of simplicity goes further than just food, equipment, and unnecessary gadgets; it goes into the matter of thoughts and objectives as well. When in the wilds, we must not carry our problems with us or the joy is lost.

Sigurd Olson

How much more deeply are we moved as we begin to appreciate the assembly of trees we call a forest, where Nature works in perfect rhythm; roots digging deep or exploring nearer the surface for food and moisture. Imperceptibly Nature builds those mighty pillars with aisles innumerable, arches multiplex, in the cathedral of the forest.

Richard St. Barbe Baker

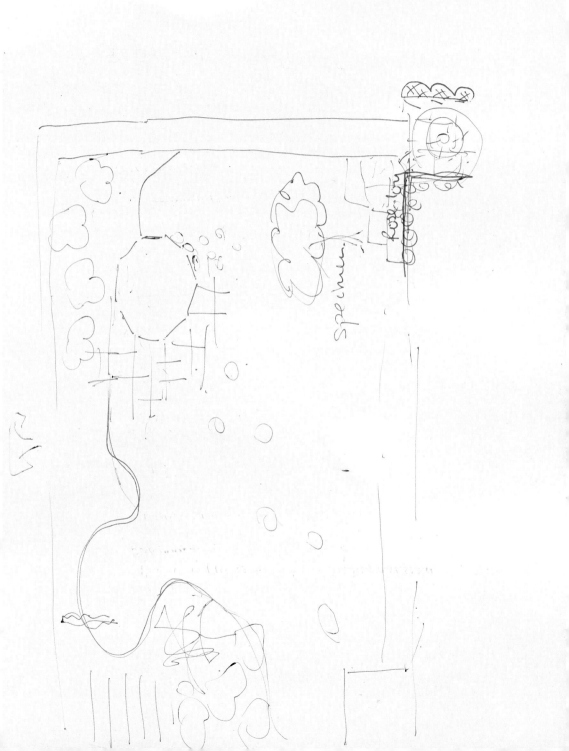

Specimen

West Wall - Corylopsis pauciflora

We simply need that wild country available to us, even if we never do more than drive to its edge and look in. For it can be a means of reassuring ourselves of our sanity as creatures, a part of the geography of hope.

Wallace Stegner

*I will not bring you flowers, but take
you by the hand and lead you to them.
Not a fistful of blossom, but a wood
dappled with primrose,
shadowed with violets.
I give you the spring.*

Pam Brown, b.1928

Honeysuckle collection
        August 2001.
Dropmore scarlet
Hall's Prolific
Serotina
Heckrottii
Haliana.

Joe's Rose - over the arch
Pink - scented 'Albertine'

~~~~~~~~~~~~~

Blueberries
Best variety
    "Southern Highbush."
High half-bush
    'Polaris'

                01202 579342
✗   " Dorset Blueby Co'

  Ken Muir   Honey Pot Farm
                0870 747 9111

    ✗   "Patriot"

BASKETS

- Levington .
- Water gel - handful
- Handful - 'Growmore'
- 'Miracle grow' } to feed -
  <u>Tom. feed</u> } to feed.
  2x weekly

? Toms general fertilizer to
  begin with
• Then a high [potash] feed
  later -

*Go now and then for fresh life – if most of humanity must go
through this town stage of development – just as divers hold their
breath and come ever and anon to the surface to breathe. Go
whether or not you have faith. Form parties, if you must be
social, to go to the snow-flowers in winter, to the sun-flowers in
summer. Anyway, go up and away for life; be fleet!*
                    John Muir (1838-1914)

Even if something is left undone, everyone must take time to sit still and watch the leaves turn.

Elizabeth Lawrence

Sylvia 05,
Linda 04

I suppose the pleasure of country life lies really in the eternally renewed evidence of the determination to live.
Vita Sackville-West
(1892-1962)

_to replace

Garrya Eliptica

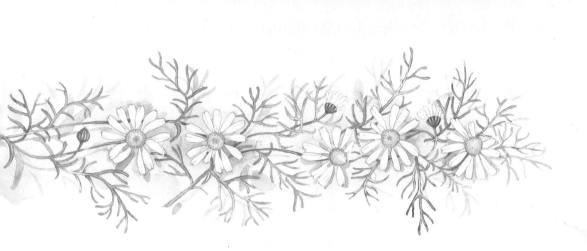

*I only went out for a walk and finally concluded to stay out till
sundown, for going out, I found, was really going in.*

John Muir (1838-1914)

I know a bank where the wild thyme blows,
Where oxlips and the nodding violet grows
Quite over-canopied with luscious woodbine,
With sweet musk-roses, and with eglantine:
          William Shakespeare (1564-1616),
          from "A Midsummer-Night's Dream"

When I first came down to the city from my mountain home, I began to wither, and wish instinctively for the vital woods and high sky. Yet I lingered month after month, plodding at "duty". At length I chanced to see a lovely goldenrod in bloom in a weedy spot alongside one of the less frequented sidewalks there. Suddenly I was aware of the ending of summer and fled. Then, once away, I saw how shrunken and lean I was, and how glad I was I had gone.

John Muir (1838-1914)

Surely there is something in the unruffled calm of nature that overawes our little anxieties and doubts: the sight of the deep-blue sky and the clustering stars above, seem to impart a quiet to the mind.

Jonathan Edwards

Those times of my life when I have been entirely at peace with myself and in tune with the world, when I have felt happy and relaxed, satisfied and light of heart, have all been spent either by the sea, or in the country.

Susan Hill, from "The Magic Apple Tree"

Come to the woods for here is rest. There is no repose like that of the green deep woods. Here grow the wallflower and the violet. The squirrel will come and sit upon your knee, the logcock will wake you in the morning. Sleep in forgetfulness of all ill.

John Muir (1838-1914)

I went to the woods because I wished to live deliberately, to front only the essential facts of life, and see if I could not learn what it had to teach, and not, when I came to die, discover that I had not lived.
  Henry David Thoreau (1817-1862)

*Nature never did betray
The heart that loved her.*
  William Wordsworth (1770-1850)

*Where would we be if humanity had never
known flowers? If they didn't exist and
had always been hidden from view . . .
our character, our morals, our aptitude
for beauty, for happiness would they
be the same?*

Maurice Maeterlinck (1862-1949)

*Every blade of grass, each leaf, each
separate floret and petal, is an inscription
speaking of hope.*

Richard Jefferies (1848-1887)

*... Those who contemplate the beauty of the
earth find reserves of strength that will endure as
long as life lasts. There is symbolic as well as actual
beauty in the migration of the birds, the ebb and
flow of the tides, the folded bud ready for the spring.
There is something infinitely healing in the
repeated refrains of nature – the assurance that
dawn comes after night, and spring after the winter.
Rachel Carson (1907-1964)*

Only by going alone in silence, without baggage, can one truly get into the heart of the wilderness. All other travel is mere dust and hotels and baggage and chatter.

John Muir (1838-1914)

O gift of God! a perfect day,
Whereon shall no man work but play,
Whereon it is enough for me
Not to be doing but to be.
　　　　　Henry Wadsworth Longfellow (1807-1882)

To make a prairie it takes a clover
And one bee,
One clover, a bee, and ... reverie!
The reverie alone will do,
If bees are few.
                    Emily Dickinson (1830-1886)

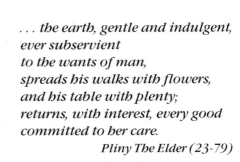

. . . the earth, gentle and indulgent,
ever subservient
to the wants of man,
spreads his walks with flowers,
and his table with plenty;
returns, with interest, every good
committed to her care.
            Pliny The Elder (23-79)

*Let love flow out from you to your surroundings.
It is not just human hearts that respond but all of
creation, for love is the life-stream of creation. It
does not matter to what the love flows; it is felt
consciously by the inner spirit of the mineral,
vegetable and animal kingdoms, making them
more vital, more part of oneness. When this love
flows from you at all times, then you are truly
expressing your divine nature.*

The Devas

I look upon the whole country in spring-time as a spacious garden, and make as many visits to a spot of daisies, or a bank of violets, as a florist does to his borders or parterres. There is not a bush in blossom within a mile of me which I am not acquainted with, nor scarce a daffodil or cowslip that withers away in my neighbourhood without my missing it.

Joseph Addison (1672-1719)

The Throstle

"Summer is coming, summer is coming.
I know it, I know it, I know it.
Light again, leaf again, life again, love again."
Yes, my wild little Poet.

Sing the new year in under the blue.
Last year you sang it as gladly.
"New, new, new, new"! Is it then so new
That you should carol so madly?

"Love again, song again, nest again, young again,"
Never a prophet so crazy!
And hardly a daisy as yet, little friend,
See there is hardly a daisy.

"Here again, here, here, here, happy year"!
O warble unchidden, unbidden!
Summer is coming, is coming, my dear,
And all the winters are hidden.

Alfred, Lord Tennyson (1809-1892)

*Here is calm so deep, grasses cease waving . . . wonderful
how completely everything in wild nature fits into us, as if truly
part and parent of us. The sun shines not on us, but in us.
The rivers flow not past, but through us, thrilling, tingling,
vibrating every fiber and cell of the substance of our bodies,
making them glide and sing.*

John Muir (1838-1914)

Happy are those who see beauty in modest spots where others see nothing. Everything is beautiful, the whole secret lies in knowing how to interpret it.

Camille Pissarro (1830-1903)

*If I were to choose the sights, the sounds, the fragrances I
most would want to see and hear and smell — among all
the delights of the open world — on a final day on earth, I
think I would choose these:*

   *the clear, ethereal song of a
   white-throated sparrow singing at dawn;
   the smell of pine trees
   in the heat of noon;
   the lonely calling of Canada geese;
   the sight of a dragon-fly
   glinting in the sunshine;
   the voice of a hermit thrush far
   in a darkening wood at evening;*

*and — most spiritual and moving of sights — the white
cathedral of a cumulus cloud floating serenely in the blue
of the sky.*

                                        Edwin Way Teale

The honisuckle that groweth wilde in every hedge, although it be very sweete, yet doe I not bring it into my garden, but let it reste in his owne place, to serve their senses that travell by it, or have no garden.

John Parkinson (1567-1650)

Thanks to the human heart by which we live
Thanks to its tenderness, its joys and fears.
To me the meanest flower that blows can give
Thoughts that do often lie too deep for tears.
               William Wordsworth (1770-1850)

To see a World in a Grain of Sand
And a heaven in a Wild Flower,
Hold Infinity in the palm of your hand
And Eternity in an hour.

      William Blake (1757-1827)

Touch the earth, love the earth, honour the earth, her plains, her valleys, her hills, and her seas; rest your spirit in her solitary places. For the gifts of life are the earth's and they are given to all, and they are the songs of birds at daybreak, Orion and the Bear, and dawn seen over ocean from the beach.

Henry Beston

Earth laughs in flowers.

Ralph Waldo Emerson (1803-1882)

... we slid through the grass and lay on our backs and just stared at the empty sky. There was nothing to do. Nothing moved or happened, nothing happened at all except summer. Small heated winds blew over our faces, dandelion seeds floated by, burnt sap and roast nettles tingled our nostrils together with the dull rust smell of dry ground. The grass was June high and had come up with a rush, a massed entanglement of species, crested with flowers and spears of wild wheat, and coiled with clambering vetches, the whole of it humming with blundering bees and flickering with scarlet butterflies. Chewing grass on our backs, the grass scaffolding the sky, the summer was all we heard; cuckoos crossed distances on chains of cries, flies buzzed and choked in the ears, and the saw-toothed chatter of mowing-machines drifted on waves of air from the fields.

Laurie Lee, b. 1914,
from "Cider With Rosie"

There is a pleasure in the pathless woods,
There is a rapture on the lonely shore,
There is society, where none intrudes,
By the deep Sea, and music in its roar:
I love not Man the less, but Nature more.
                              Lord Byron (1788-1824)

It seems to me I'd like to go
Where bells don't ring, nor whistles blow,
Nor clocks don't strike, nor gongs sound,
And I'd have stillness all around.

Not real stillness, but just the trees,
Low whispering, or the hum of bees,
Or brooks faint babbling over stones,
In strangely, softly tangled tones.

Or maybe a cricket or katydid,
Or the songs of birds in the hedges hid,
Or just some such sweet sound as these,
To fill a tired heart with ease. . . .

Nixon Waterman, extract from
"Far From the Madding Crowd"

I will exchange a city
for a sunset,
The tramp of legions
for a wind's wild cry;
And all the braggart thrusts
of steel triumphant
For one far summit,
blue against the sky.

Marie Blake

. . . in wildness is the preservation of the World.

Henry David Thoreau (1817-1862)

What does he plant who plants a tree?
He plants cool shade and tender rain,
And seed and bud of days to be.
                    Henry C. Bunner

Glory be to God for dappled things —
For skies of couple-colour as a brinded cow;
For rose-moles all in stipple upon trout that swim;
Fresh-firecoal chestnut-falls; finches' wings;
Landscape plotted and pieced — fold, fallow and plough;
And all trades, their gear and tackle and trim. . . .
  Gerard Manley Hopkins (1844-1899), from "Pied Beauty"

It were happy if we studied nature more in natural things;
and acted according to nature, whose rules are few, plain,
and most reasonable.
  William Penn (1644-1718)

Sympathy with nature is an evidence of perfect health. You cannot perceive beauty but with a serene mind.

Henry David Thoreau (1817-1862)

This grand show is eternal. It is always sunrise somewhere; the dew is never all dried at once; a shower is forever falling; vapor is ever rising. Eternal sunrise, eternal sunset, eternal dawn and gloaming, on sea and continents and islands, each in its turn, as the round earth rolls.

John Muir (1838-1914)

*After you have exhausted what
there is in business, politics,
conviviality, and so on – have
found that none of these finally
satisfy, or permanently wear –
what remains?
Nature remains.*

Walt Whitman (1819-1892)

*Come forth into the light
of things. Let Nature be
your teacher.*
　　　　　William Wordsworth
　　　　　　(1770-1850)

*One touch of nature
makes the whole
world kin.*
　　　　　William Shakespeare
　　　　　　(1564-1616)

*All my life through, the
new sights of Nature made
me rejoice like a child.*
　　　Marie Curie (1867-1934)

The forest is generous. It can spare man some trees for his timber, and all the time the silent forest is busy, giving us our oxygen, taking away the surplus carbon dioxide, helping to remove the pollutants. Even visually the trees are beautiful and stress-relieving, but in their silence they do much more. Their only voice is the wind; they have no vote and are defenceless.

Sir Frank Fraser Darling

Man cannot be independent of nature. In one way or another he must live in relation to it, and there are only two alternatives: the way of the frontiersman, whose response to nature was to dominate it, to assert his presence in it by destroying it; or the way of Thoreau, who went to the natural places to become quiet in them, to learn from them, to be restored by them.

Wendell Berry

One impulse from a vernal wood
May teach you more of man;
Of moral evil and of good,
Than all the sages can.
William Wordsworth
(1770-1850),
from "The Tables Turned"